COLLECTABLES

Fairy Charms

This is a STAR FIRE book

STAR FIRE BOOKS
Crabtree Hall, Crabtree Lane
Fulham, London SW6 6TY
United Kingdom

www.star-fire.co.uk

First published 2008

08 10 12 11 09

1 3 5 7 9 10 8 6 4 2

Star Fire is part of The Foundry Creative Media Company Limited

© The Foundry 2008

The right of Ulysses Brave to be identified as the author of this
work has been asserted by him in accordance with the Copyright, Designs
and Patents Act 1988.

The CIP record for this book is available from the British Library.

ISBN: 978 1 84786 194 8

Printed in China

Thanks to: Chelsea Edwards, Chris Herbert,
Gemma Walters and Nick Wells

Picture credits
Courtesy of Christie's Images Ltd: 7 John Atkinson Grimshaw (1836–93) *Iris*, 1876; 29 John Atkinson Grimshaw
(1836–93) *Iris*, 1876; 43 Etheline E. Dell (fl. 1885–91) *Midsummer Fairies*; 49, 72 Amelia Jane Murray, Lady Oswald
(1800–96) *Fairies Floating Downstream in a Peapod*; 53 Amelia Jane Murray, Lady Oswald (1800–96) *A Fairy Waving her
Magic Wand Across a Stormy Sea*; 56 Richard Doyle (1824–83) *The Altar Cup in Aagerup: The Moment of Departure*;
69 John Atkinson Grimshaw (1836–93) *Autumn – Dame Autumn Hath a Mournful Face* (detail), 1871. **Courtesy of
Sotheby's Picture Library**: 19 John Atkinson Grimshaw (1836–93) *Spirit of the Night*, 1879. **Courtesy of The
Bridgeman Art Library**: 24 Richard Doyle (1824–83). *Dancing Fairies* (detail); 30 Henry Meynell Rheam (1859–1920)
The Fairy Wood, 1903; 1, 3, 37 Walter Jenks Morgan (1847–1924) 'Where Rural Fays and Fairies Dwell'; 65 © Leeds
Museums and Galleries (City Art Gallery) UK *Iris*, 1886 John Atkinson Grimshaw (1836–93). **Courtesy of Fotolia**:
33 © Joe Gough; 4, 41 © GRIP; 47 © Patrick Hardy; 60 © dotshock; 66 © Rosmarie Mitterlechner. **Courtesy of
(Private Collection) Foundry Arts**: 9, 17, 62; 13, 51, 71 Illustrations by Warwick Goble (1862–1943) from *The Waterbabies*;
11, 15, 21, 23, 27, 35, 39, 45, 55, 59 Illustrations by Arthur Rackham (1867–1939) from *Peter Pan in Kensington Gardens*.

Every effort has been made to contact all copyright holders. The publishers would be pleased to hear
if any oversights or omissions have occurred.

COLLECTABLES

Fairy Charms

Posy Carpenter

STAR FIRE

FOREWORD

Fairies have weaved their spell on us for
generations. They reach out through their
deep, celtic roots through medieval times and
find their peak of nostalgic fascination in the
Victorian era. This wonderful little book
allows you to dip in and out of magical
illustrations, potions, recipes and poems, all of
which stir the dreams within us. Created to
enjoy and to keep by your side, we hope
that FAIRY CHARMS will bring you years
of quiet pleasure.

FAIRY BREAD

Come up here, O dusty feet!
  Here is fairy bread to eat.
Here in my retiring room,
  Children, you may dine
On the golden smell of broom
  And the shade of pine;
And when you have eaten well,
Fairy stories hear and tell.

Robert Louis Stevenson (1850–94)

FAIRY PLANTS: MUSHROOM

The fairies use mushrooms as tables and
stools. But you must beware the species
Amanita (the red and white mushroom) as
they are very poisonous.

❊

Music and dancing are among fairies'
favourite pastimes. At night they come
out of their homes and dance the
night away.

FAIRY PLANTS: SAFFRON CROCUS

The stamens from these autumn-flowering crocuses constitute the herb saffron. Any dish that is prepared with saffron is a favourite of the fairies. It is also used as a dye that will turn cloth a royal gold colour, and therefore is very valuable to the fairies.

IN FAIRYLAND

The fairy poet takes a sheet
Of moonbeam, silver white;
His ink is dew from daisies sweet,
His pen a point of light.
My love I know is fairer far
Than his, (though she is fair),
And we should dwell where fairies are,
For I could praise her there.

Joyce Kilmer (1886–1918)

The most special date in the fairies'
calendar is Midsummer's Eve (24 June),
because this is when they are at
their merriest.

EPICUREAN

In Childhood's unsuspicious hours
The fairies crown'd my head with flowers.

Youth came: I lay at Beauty's feet;
She smil'd and said my song was sweet.

Then Age, and Love no longer mine,
My brows I shaded with the vine.

With flowers and love and wine and song,
O Death! life hath not been too long.

William James Linton (1812–97)

PLANTS TO USE TO BREAK
FAIRY SPELLS 1

FOUR-LEAF CLOVER
Has the power to break fairy spells and,
if carried in your hat, allows you to see
invisible fairies.

THYME
Drinking a potion made of thyme can
enable you to see fairies and will protect
you from fairy mischief.

TYPES OF FAIRY: BROWNIE

Brownies are small, hardworking elf-like creatures that live in houses and barns. They are said to come out at night, and finish the housework that has been left undone.

The faries' favourite time to dance is when there is a full moon. As the sun rises in the morning they vanish.

FAIRY PLANTS: FOXGLOVE

There are many fairy legends surrounding the foxglove. In one such story using the juice of a foxglove could help you get your child back after the fairies had taken them. Another claims that picking a foxglove would cause great offence to the fairies.

BUBBLING POTION

Cauldron - Water - Baking Soda - Vinegar
Tablespoon - Cup - Pan or Tray

1. Place the cauldron on a pan or tray, to avoid spilling potion everywhere.
2. Fill the cauldron with two tablespoons of water and stir in a tablespoon of baking soda till it dissolves.
3. Measure two tablespoons of vinegar into a separate cup.
4. Pour the vinegar all at once into the water and baking soda mixture and watch your potion bubble up!

FAIRY PLANTS: BLUEBELL

Fairies are summoned to their
midnight revels and dances by the
ringing of these tiny flowers.

THE FAIRY BEAM UPON YOU

The fairy beam upon you,
The stars to glisten on you,
   A moon of light
   In the noon of night,
Till the firedrake hath o'er-gone you.
The wheel of fortune guide you,
The boy with the bow beside you
Run aye in the way
   Till the bird of day
And the luckier lote betide you.

Ben Jonson (1572–1637)

TYPES OF FAIRY: ELF

Elves were originally found in Germanic
and Scandinavian folklore. There were
two kinds of elves – the light elves, who
were fair, and the dark elves, who were
darker than pitch.

The music of the fairies is much more
melodious than any mortal music and there are
many songs and tunes which are said to have
originated from the fairies. Many of the
pipers and fiddlers of Europe learned
their songs from the fairies.

FAIRY FLOWER OIL

1 dram elder oil ~ 1 dram lavender oil
a few dried rose buds

1. Warm slowly in an enamel saucepan.
2. Leave to cool.
3. Pour into magic bottles and use in spellwork and rituals.

FAIRY PLANTS: FERN

Pixie fairies are especially fond of ferns. One
story tells of a young woman who accidentally
sat on a fern, and instantly a fairy man
appeared and forced her to promise to watch
over his fairy son and remain in Fairyland for a
year and a day.

UNWRITTEN POEMS

Fairy spirits of the breeze –
Frailer nothing is than these.
Fancies born we know not where –
In the heart or in the air;
Wandering echoes blown unsought
From far crystal peaks of thought;
Shadows, fading at the dawn,
Ghosts of feeling dead and gone:
Alas! Are all fair things that live
Still lovely and still fugitive?

William Winter (1836–1917)

TYPES OF FAIRY: GOBLIN

Goblins are mischievous, malicious
fairies that live in small caves and
underground caverns.

PLANTS TO USE TO BREAK FAIRY SPELLS 2

ST JOHN'S WORT

This healing herb can be used to break fairy spells and cure illnesses caused by fairy darts. However, some stories say that the plant is sacred to fairies and should never be stepped on.

ENGLISH DAISY

Placing a daisychain around a child's neck can protect them from meddling fairies.

TYPES OF FAIRY: CORRIGAN

Corrigans are beautiful maidens by day and ugly hags by night. If a man should marry them, they will remain in their beautiful state.

TYPES OF FAIRY: SELKIE

Selkies have the appearance of seals,
but can shed their skin and transform
into humans.

※

THE RESCUE FAIRY

At the pitchest black of blackest night,
Where storms do rage their stormy fight,
There are fairies slight who, fair and white,
Will humans save from drowning fright:

But during daylight the fair spirits rest,
So ships beware, shipwrecks at night are best.

TYPES OF FAIRY: PIXIE

Pixies are tiny elf-like fairies, specific to
the folklore of southwestern England.

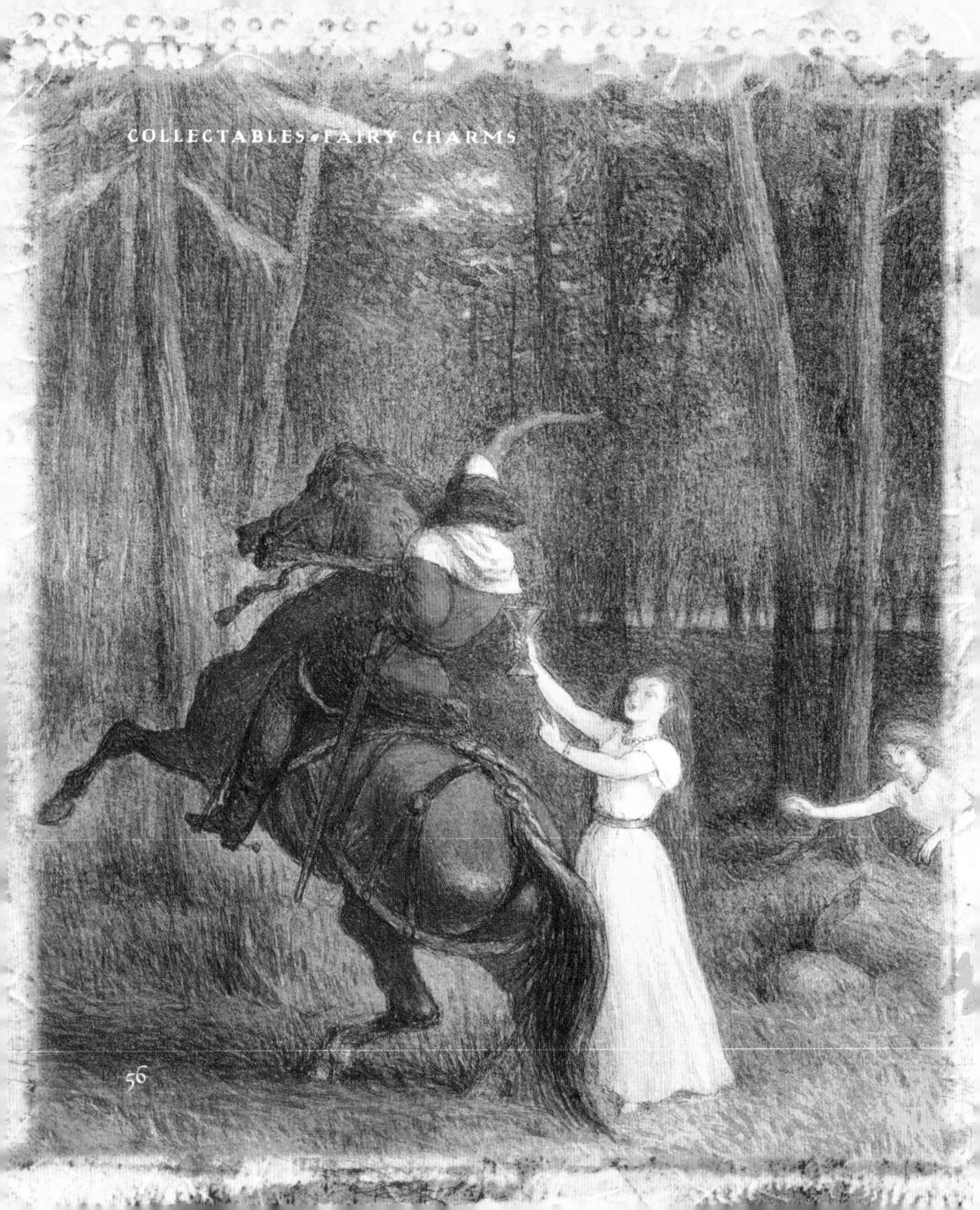

Many mortals desired to see the magnificent dancing fairies at night. But this was a very dangerous desire, as if the fairies lured and trapped the mortal they would force them to dance until they collapsed of exhaustion.

TYPES OF FAIRY: KOBOLD

A kobold is a small goblin-like
spirit, who can be both helpful
and mischievous.

FAIRY PLANTS: PRIMROSE

The primrose is a key into Fairyland. There is a
German legend about a little girl who found a
doorway covered in flowers, and when she
touched it with a primrose, the door opened up,
leading to an enchanted fairy castle.

FAIRY CHANT

'Come out of your Fairy Bower. Come
upon this golden hour. Come to me,
I beg you please. Fairies dancing
upon the breeze.'

RAGWORT, CABBAGE STALKS, GRASS AND STRAW

All of these plants are used by fairies as transportation, in much the same way as witches use their broomsticks.

TYPES OF FAIRY: MOSSMAN

Mossmen are dressed in moss and have big
flowers in their hair. They know the healing
properties of everything in the forest.

EXTRACT FROM
MIDSUMMER NIGHT'S DREAM,
ACT THREE, SCENE TWO

Captain of our fairy band,
Helena is here at hand;
And the youth, mistook by me,
Pleading for a lover's fee.
Shall we their fond pageant see?
Lord, what fools these mortals be!

William Shakespeare (1564–1616)

SOME FAIRY CALLS

Sit where the cat sits. Cross your toes.
Close your eyes. And smell a rose.

Then under your breath say:

'I believe in fairies, sure as day.'

'Gadflykins! Gladtrypins! Gutterpuss and Cass!
Come to me fairly. Each lad and lass!

Come back soon!